Teaching and Learning
Key Stage 2
Differentiated Activity Book

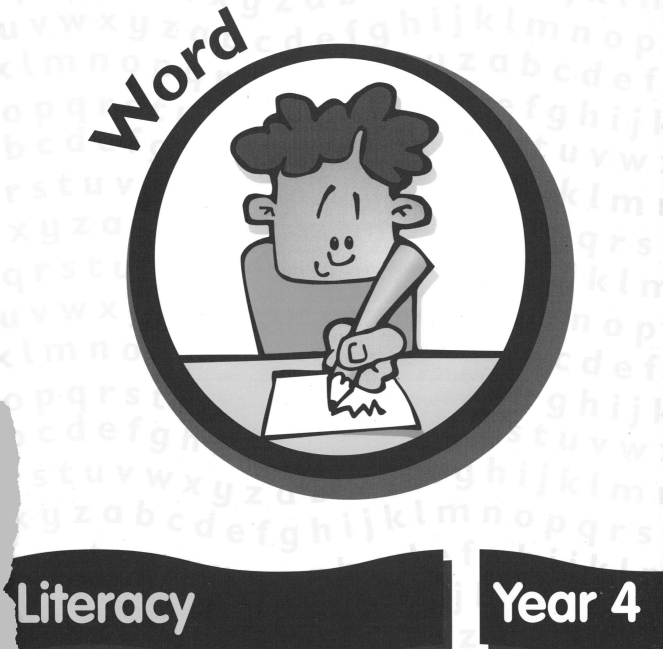

Word

Literacy

Year 4

Contents

Introduction

Differentiated Activity Books:

- support the teaching of the Literacy Hour
- help meet the majority of the objectives of the National Literacy Strategy Framework
- contain 30 units of work, sufficient for one school year
- are straightforward and easy to use
- have a clear teaching focus
- contain differentiated activities for each objective at foundation, intermediate and challenging levels of difficulty.

Features of the Word Level Teaching Units

Teaching objective

Unit number

Teaching focus

Differentiated activity— foundation level

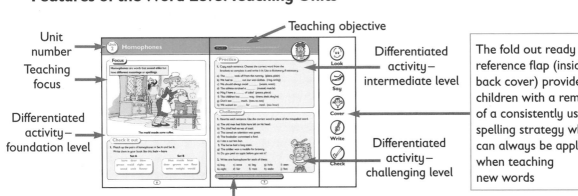

Differentiated activity— intermediate level

Differentiated activity— challenging level

The fold out ready reference flap (inside back cover) provides children with a reminder of a consistently useful spelling strategy which can always be applied when teaching new words

Reminder of main objective of the unit

Using the Differentiated Activity Books

A Variety of Uses

The books may be used to:
- introduce and teach individual National Literacy Strategy Framework objectives independently
- introduce individual National Literacy Strategy Framework objectives prior to studying them during Text Level work
- consolidate, develop and extend National Literacy Strategy Framework objectives studied during Text Level work
- provide work for whole class, group or individual work
- provide work for follow-up homework assignments.

Class Work

The Teaching focus provides a clear explanation of each objective with examples for discussion. Appropriate activities may be chosen from the range of differentiated tasks for discussion, or to work through, with the class.

Group and Individual Work

The Differentiated Activity Books are ideal for group and individual work. Work on the same objective may be realistically matched appropriately to individual children's abilities, allowing children to work independently.

Homework

The material in the books provides an ideal solution to meaningful homework assignments that can be differentiated appropriately for each pupil.

Focus

We can break words down into smaller parts, called **syllables**.
In two-syllable words containing a **double consonant**, we make
the syllable break **between** the two consonants.

Ten/nis, Den/nis?

Check it out

1. Copy these syllable sums. Write the answers in your book.

a) shop + ping = _____

b) swim + mer = _____

c) rub + bish = _____

d) fat + ten = _____

e) chat + ty = _____

f) thin + nest = _____

g) wag + ging = _____

h) beg + gar = _____

i) hap + py = _____

j) sup + ply = _____

k) sud + den = _____

l) mar + ry = _____

2. Choose six of the words you have made. Make up some sentences of your
own, each containing one of the words.

Objective ~ to spell two-syllable words containing double consonants

Practice

1. Find all the two-syllable words containing a double consonant in the box. Split the words into two syllables and write them in your book. Do it like this: **assist = as/sist**

runner	disgust	hollow	intend
ugly	tunnel	rabbit	kingdom
label	offend	clammy	pillow
attempt	hungry	spider	poem
puppet	smuggler	curry	lantern

Challenger

1. Copy the words below. Try to think of a different double consonant to complete each word and write them in.

a) co __ __ ect

b) fu __ __ el

c) fo __ __ ow

d) pa __ __ age

e) bu __ __ on

f) ca __ __ age

g) a __ __ oy

h) su __ __ ess

i) sto __ __ er

j) o __ __ end

k) su __ __ est

l) sni __ __ le

m) sa __ __ le

n) no __ __ le

o) pu __ __ ing

2. Now write each word again, splitting it into syllables.
Do it like this: **correct = cor + rect**

So – what have you learned about two-syllable words containing a double consonant?

Focus

> **Homophones** are words that **sound alike** but have **different meanings** or **spellings**.

The **maid made** some coffee.

Check it out

1. Match up the pairs of homophones in Set A and Set B.
   Write them in your book like this: **hair – hare**

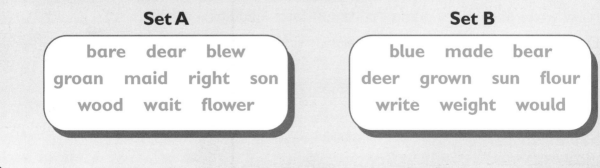

Set A	Set B
bare dear blew groan maid right son wood wait flower	blue made bear deer grown sun flour write weight would

Practice

1. Copy each sentence. Choose the correct word from the
brackets to complete it and write it in. Use a dictionary, if necessary.

a) The _____ took off from the runway. (plane, plain)

b) We had to _____ out our wet clothes. (ring, wring)

c) We should always avoid _____. (waste, waist)

d) The athlete strained a _____. (mussel, muscle)

e) May I have a _____ of cake? (peace, piece)

f) The children lost _____ way. (there, their, they're)

g) Don't eat _____ much. (two, to, too)

h) We waited an _____ for _____ meal. (our, hour)

Challenger

1. Rewrite each sentence. Use the correct word in place of the misspelled word.

a) The old man had little hare left on his head.

b) The thief had nerves of steal.

c) The cereal on television was great.

d) The footballer committed a fowl.

e) I ate a current bun.

f) The horse had a long main.

g) The soldier won a meddle for bravery.

h) Do you peal an apple before you eat it?

2. Write one homophone for each of these:

a) boy   c) none   e) key   g) hole   i) seen

b) night   d) fair   f) root   h) stake   j) feet

So – what have you learned about homophones?

Focus

We can change many verbs into the **past tense** by adding the **suffixes ed** or **ing**.

The teacher shout**ed** at Tom.
She was shout**ing** very loudly.

Tom smil**ed** at the teacher.
He was smil**ing** very sweetly.

Sometimes we do not have to change the spelling of the root verb.

If a verb ends in **e**, we usually drop the **e** and add **ing** or **ed**.

Check it out

1. Copy and complete this table.

Root verb	+ ing	+ ed
walk	walking	
call		called
	jumping	jumped
climb		climbed
laugh		
		looked
	kicking	
open		
crash		
		sketched

Practice

1. Add **ing** and **ed** to each of these verbs.

Do it like this: **smile – smiling – smiled**

a) rake   c) gape   e) save   g) like   i) dine

b) flame   d) skate   f) glide   h) file   j) dive

2. Write what the root word of each of these verbs is.

Do it like this: **wiping – wipe**

a) stoned   c) joked   e) voted   g) ruled   i) excused

b) hoping   d) closing   f) fuming   h) amusing   j) tuning

Challenger

1. Copy the sentences below. Choose the correct form of the verb to complete each sentence.

a) The teacher _____ what he said. (believe)

b) The sculptor was _____ a piece of wood. (shape)

c) My friend _____ in a whisper. (answer)

d) The athlete was just _____ her run. (complete)

e) The sausages _____ in the pan. (sizzle)

f) I didn't know what was _____. (happen)

g) The girl was _____ about in the dark. (stumble)

h) The musician _____ some lovely music. (compose)

i) The baby was _____ an apple. (bite)

j) My mum _____ my glass to the brim. (fill)

So – what have you learned about ending verbs with 'ing' and 'ed'?

Focus

We can change many verbs into the **past tense** by adding the suffixes **ed** or **ing**.

Emma was **zipping** up her coat.
It was cold so she **zipped** it up.

The baby was **crying**.
He **cried** until he was fed.

With short verbs ending in a vowel and consonant, we often have to **double** the final consonant before adding **ing** or **ed**.

If a verb ends in a consonant plus **y** we just add **ing**.
For example: **cry – crying**
When we add **ed**, we have to **change** the **y** to **i** before adding **ed**.

Check it out

1. Copy and complete this table.

Root verb	+ ing	+ ed
hop	hopping	
lag		lagged
	pinning	pinned
nod	nodding	
hug		
		rammed
	batting	
dip		
bob		
		hummed

Practice

1. Add **ing** and **ed** to each of these verbs.

Do it like this: **cry – crying – cried**

a) spy   c) rely   e) apply   g) occupy   i) multiply

b) try   d) deny   f) reply   h) supply   j) dry

2. Write what the root word of each of these verbs is.

Do it like this: **cried – cry**

a) spied   c) emptied   e) defying   g) buried   i) studying

b) flying   d) copied   f) terrifying   h) occupied   j) married

Challenger

1. Copy the sentences below. Choose the correct form of the verb to complete each sentence.

a) He _____ to school because he was late. (hurry)

b) The poor man was _____ in the street. (beg)

c) The old lady was _____ a black handbag. (carry)

d) Alice _____ hard for her exams. (study)

e) When the show began, the lights _____. (dim)

f) The cleaner _____ the dirty floor. (mop)

g) Mr Amin _____ some new cupboards. (fit)

h) Two _____ by two equals four. (multiply)

i) Vicky was _____ her sore head. (rub)

j) Tom's mum was _____ by the mess in his bedroom. (horrify)

So – what have you learned about ending verbs with 'ing' and 'ed'?

Focus

The past tense of some verbs is not always written as you would expect. We call these verbs **irregular**.

I **go** to a junior school.   A few years ago, I **went** to an infant school.

Check it out

1. Match up the present and past tenses of these irregular verbs.
Write them like this:
drink – drank

Present tense	Past tense
drink	broke
am	grew
break	drank
wear	taught
think	was
shake	did
grow	thought
do	left
leave	wore
teach	shook

Practice

1. Copy these sentences. Complete them by using the past tense of the verb in brackets.

a) The man _____ the bell. (ring)

b) I _____ in a whisper. (speak)

c) The children _____ their bikes to the shops. (ride)

d) The child _____ a lovely picture. (draw)

e) The lion _____ from behind a bush. (spring)

f) Edward _____ all his dinner. (eat)

g) We _____ lots of animals on the farm. (see)

h) The water _____ in the pond. (freeze)

Challenger

1. Rewrite these sentences. Change the underlined verbs into the past tense.

a) I <u>rise</u> early and <u>choose</u> a T-shirt to wear.

b) I <u>get</u> dressed and <u>take</u> my book downstairs.

c) We <u>give</u> the dog a bone and he <u>bites</u> it.

d) My mum <u>catches</u> a bus to work.

e) The child <u>falls</u> over and <u>breaks</u> a leg.

f) The clock <u>strikes</u> twelve as the boy <u>leaves</u>.

g) The lady <u>sings</u> a song as she <u>digs</u> the garden.

h) The princess <u>goes</u> to the ball and <u>wears</u> a beautiful gown.

So – what have you learned about irregular verbs?

Focus

A **prefix** is a group of letters we put **in front** of a word.

A **suffix** is a group of letters we add to the **end** of a word.

Prefixes and suffixes **change the meaning** or **purpose** of the word.

The letters **al** may be used as **both** a prefix and a suffix.

I have **al**ways been music**al**.

Notice that **al** only ever has **one l** when used as a prefix or a suffix.

Check it out

1. Complete these **al** words and write them in your book.

a) __ __ways   c) __ __most   e) __ __one

b) __ __ready   d) __ __so   f) __ __though

2. Copy the sentences below. Choose an **al** word to complete each one sensibly.

a) It was _____ lunchtime when I finished.

b) When everyone went, I was _____ .

c) I _____ get up early.

d) When I got a lolly my friend _____ wanted one.

e) I tried hard _____ I knew the spellings were too hard.

f) I was _____ dressed when Mum called me.

Practice

1. Change these nouns into adjectives by adding the suffix **al**.

Do it like this: **music – musical**

a) magic   c) person   e) coast   g) mechanic

b) accident   d) comic   f) season   h) topic

2. Find the eight **al** words in the puzzle.

Copy them into your book.

Say if the **al** is used as a suffix

or a prefix each time.

q	u	e	r	a	l	w	a	y	s	t	y	u	p
d	m	a	g	i	c	a	l	v	b	n	m	x	z
a	s	d	k	j	a	l	r	e	a	d	y	b	v
z	x	a	l	t	h	o	u	g	h	m	p	u	r
c	o	a	s	t	a	l	k	h	g	f	s	a	q
l	k	j	h	g	f	o	r	i	g	i	n	a	l
t	g	r	e	d	a	l	o	n	e	n	b	c	s
m	a	t	h	e	m	a	t	i	c	a	l	d	w

Challenger

1. Write what the root word of each of these **al** words is.

Do it like this: **mechanical – mechanic**

a) mathematical   d) electrical   g) biblical

b) tropical   e) physical   h) hysterical

c) universal   f) theatrical   i) original

2. Choose five of the words above. Make up some

sentences, each containing one of the words.

So – what have you learned about 'al' when used as a prefix and a suffix?

Focus

A **suffix** is a group of letters we add to the end of a word.
Suffixes **change the meaning** or **purpose** of the word.

enjoy – enjoy**ment**

The video game gave me a lot of enjoy**ment**.

The suffix **ment** is quite common.
It is often used to change a **verb** into a **noun**.

Check it out

1. Do these syllable sums.
   Write the words you make in your book.

a) move + ment = _____   e) am + use + ment = _____

b) in + volve + ment = _____   f) im + prove + ment = _____

c) a + gree + ment = _____   g) man + age + ment = _____

d) em + ploy + ment = _____   h) ar + gu + ment = _____

2. Now write all the **ment** words you have made in alphabetical order.

Practice

1. Copy these **ment** nouns in your book. Write the word from which each came. Do it like this: **entertainment – entertain**

a) amusement   e) development

b) astonishment   f) disagreement

c) arrangement   g) establishment

d) government   h) merriment

2. Split each word into syllables. Do it like this:

entertainment = en + ter + tain + ment

Challenger

1. Rewrite these words correctly. Use a dictionary to help.

a) arguement   d) enviroment   g) temparament

b) goverment   e) advertisment   h) developement

c) parlament   f) excitment   i) assinment

2. Choose five of the words above. Make up some sentences, each containing one of the words.

So – what have you learned about the 'ment' suffix?

Focus

A **suffix** is a group of letters we add to the end of a word.
Suffixes **change the meaning** or **purpose** of the word.

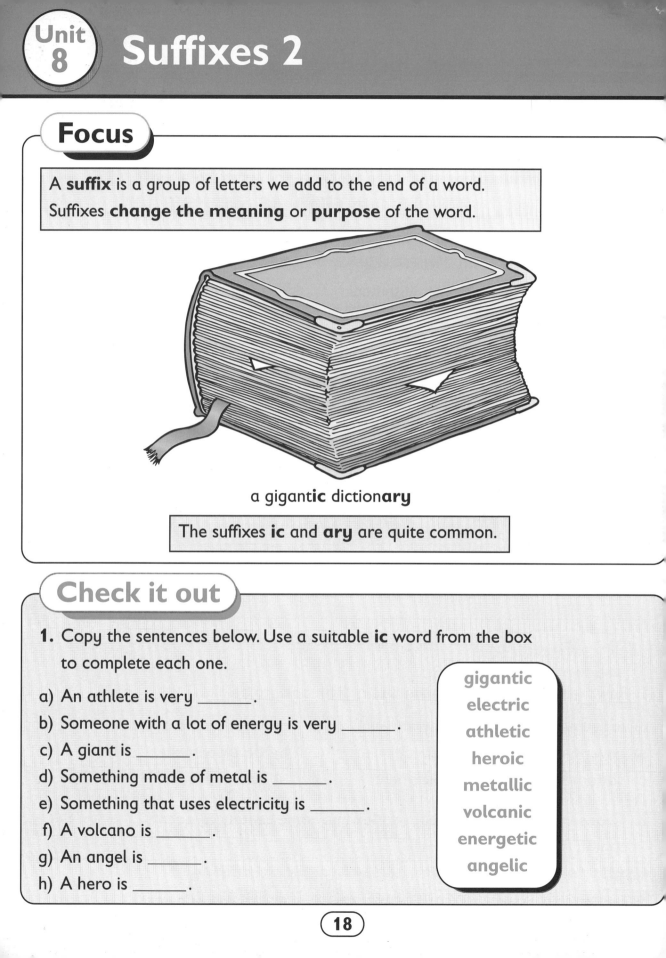

a gigant**ic** diction**ary**

The suffixes **ic** and **ary** are quite common.

Check it out

1. Copy the sentences below. Use a suitable **ic** word from the box to complete each one.

a) An athlete is very _____.

b) Someone with a lot of energy is very _____.

c) A giant is _____.

d) Something made of metal is _____.

e) Something that uses electricity is _____.

f) A volcano is _____.

g) An angel is _____.

h) A hero is _____.

gigantic
electric
athletic
heroic
metallic
volcanic
energetic
angelic

Practice

1. Copy the words below. Use either **ary** or **ic** to complete each one.
Use a dictionary, if necessary.

a) majest____

b) custom____

c) dynam____

d) poet____

e) moment____

f) necess____

g) elast____

h) realist____

i) milit____

j) artist____

k) automat____

l) station____

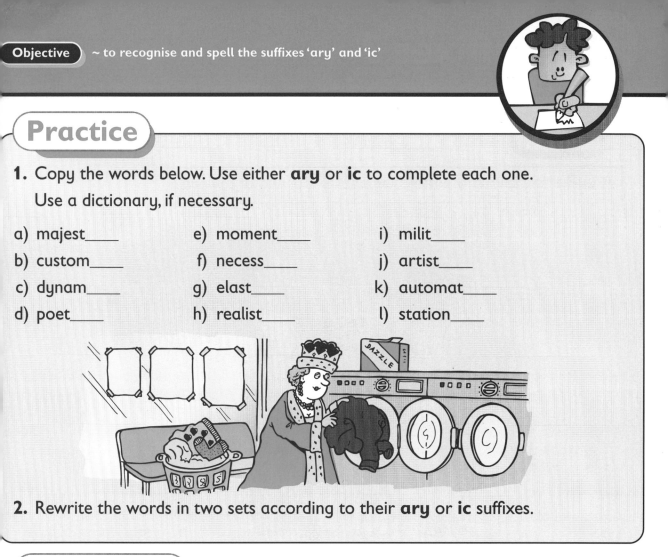

2. Rewrite the words in two sets according to their **ary** or **ic** suffixes.

Challenger

1. These **ary** and **ic** words are all nouns. Each word has got the wrong ending.
Rewrite each word correctly. Do it like this: **libric** should be **library**

a) libric

b) comary

c) arithmetary

d) dictionic

e) secretic

f) mechanary

g) glossic

h) magary

i) critary

j) tributic

2. Write a definition for each word. Use a dictionary to help you.

So – what have you learned about the suffixes 'ary' and 'ic'?

Focus

A **suffix** is a group of letters we add to the end of a word.

dark + ness =
dark**ness**

neighbour + hood =
neighbour**hood**

friend + ship =
friend**ship**

Check it out

1. Add the suffix to each word. Write the words you make in your book.

a)
ill
fit → **ness**
quiet
good

b)
child
boy → **hood**
girl
adult

c)
fellow
leader → **ship**
hard
friend

2. Now write each set of words you have made in alphabetical order.

Practice

1. Copy the table below. Sort the words in the box into the correct columns.

brightness	lordship	sickness	manhood
parenthood	blindness	hardship	fellowship
childhood	leadership	narrowness	neighbourhood

ness words	**hood** words	**ship** words

2. Now write all the root words. Take the suffixes off each word in the box. Do it like this: **brightness – ness = bright**

Challenger

1. Choose from the suffixes **ness**, **hood** or **ship** to complete each word below.

a) bright_____

b) sticki_____

c) girl_____

d) hard_____

e) scholar_____

f) parent_____

g) nervous_____

h) weari_____

i) child_____

j) happi_____

k) holi_____

l) neighbour_____

2. Choose six of the words you have made. Make up some sentences of your own, each containing one of the words.

3. Write a **ness** word that is opposite to:

a) stickiness

b) darkness

c) sadness

d) goodness

e) noisiness

f) dirtiness

So – what have you learned about the suffixes 'ness', 'hood' and 'ship'?

Focus

A **definition** is the **meaning** of a word.
Dictionaries give us the definitions of words.

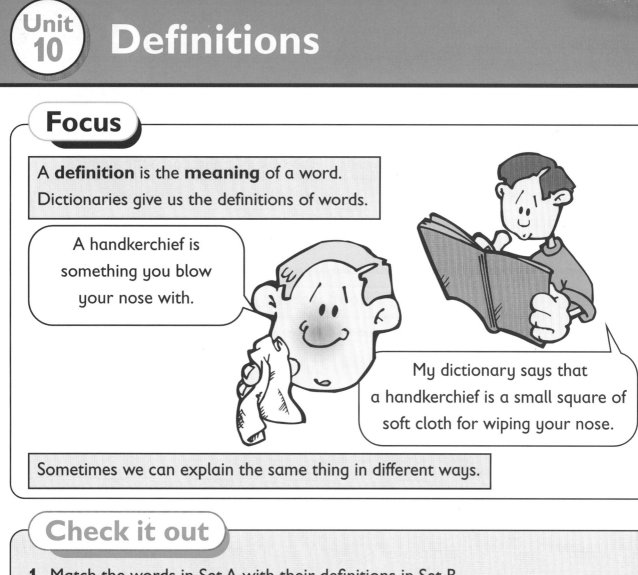

A handkerchief is something you blow your nose with.

My dictionary says that a handkerchief is a small square of soft cloth for wiping your nose.

Sometimes we can explain the same thing in different ways.

Check it out

1. Match the words in Set A with their definitions in Set B.
Write them both in your book.

Set A

flood
couch
razor
key
battle
towel
small
harp

Set B

Something with which to open locks.
An instrument for shaving.
A great deal of water that covers normally dry land.
Someone or something that is not very big.
A long seat for several people to sit on.
A fight between groups of armed forces.
A stringed instrument played by plucking with the fingers.
A piece of cloth you use to dry yourself after washing.

Practice

1. Copy these definitions in your book. Finish them in your own words.

a) A wardrobe is a piece of _____ for storing _____.

b) An ostrich is a _____ that cannot _____, with a long _____
and long _____.

c) A guitar is a musical _____ with _____.

d) A serviette is a small square of _____ used to protect
your _____ while you eat.

e) A clipboard is a piece of stiff _____ with a _____ at the top
to keep _____ in place.

2. Copy these definitions. Write which word you think is being defined.

a) _____   Measures the time.

b) _____   Slippery liquid used to make machines run smoothly.

c) _____   A dry wasteland where few things grow.

d) _____   A warning given when there is danger.

e) _____   A place where grapes are grown to make wine.

Check your answers in a dictionary.

Challenger

1. Make up your own definitions for the following words.

a) giraffe   e) bunk beds   i) barn

b) cathedral   f) tweezers   j) trough

c) dew   g) thermometer   k) pyre

d) surgeon   h) kilt   l) saddle

So – what have you learned about definitions?

Focus

Many **books** are arranged in **alphabetical order**, for example: dictionaries and thesauruses.

| pa**p**er | pa**r**ty | pa**v**ement | pa**w**s |

These words are organised in **alphabetical order** according to their **third** letter.

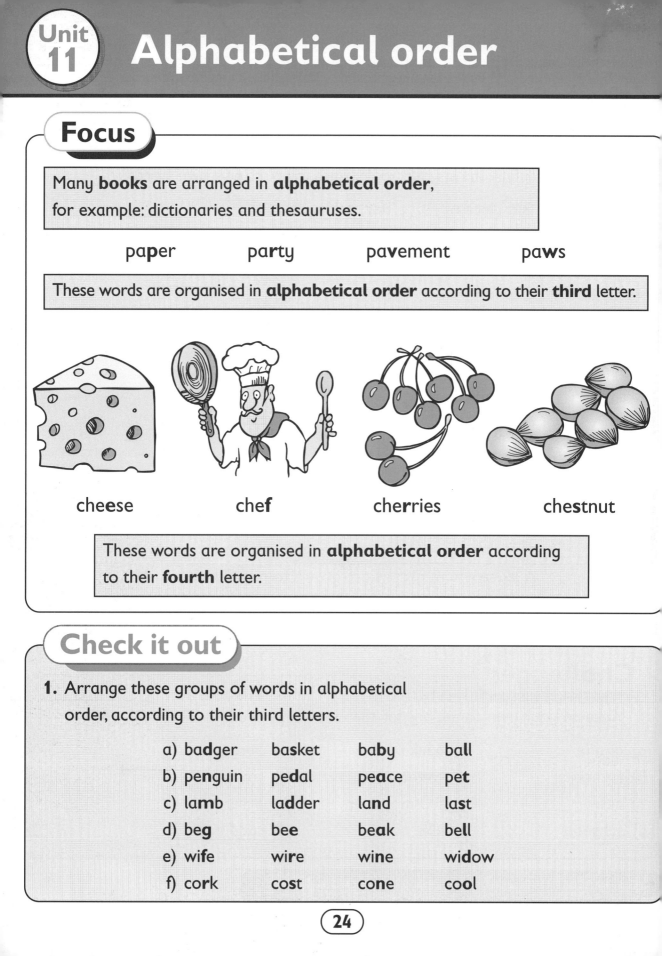

| cheese | chef | cherries | chestnut |

These words are organised in **alphabetical order** according to their **fourth** letter.

Check it out

1. Arrange these groups of words in alphabetical order, according to their third letters.

a) badger   basket   baby   ball

b) penguin   pedal   peace   pet

c) lamb   ladder   land   last

d) beg   bee   beak   bell

e) wife   wire   wine   widow

f) cork   cost   cone   cool

Practice

1. Think of a different letter to complete the words in each set. Then write the words in alphabetical order. The first one has been done for you.

a) sa_**v**_age   sa_**i**_nt   sa_**c**_k   sa**m**ple → **sack, saint, sample, savage**

b) wa__e   wa__te   wa__m   wa__er

c) te__t   te__ch   te__der   te__her

d) di__e   di__ty   di__ger   di__ficult

e) pe__   pe__   pe__   pe__

f) ru__   ru__   ru__   ru__

g) co__   co__   co__   co__

h) ca__   ca__   ca__   ca__

Challenger

1. Rewrite these sets of words in alphabetical order, according to their fourth letters.

a) bear   beaver   beast   beaten

b) candle   cane   canal   canyon

c) helping   hello   helicopter   held

d) shop   shoe   shore   shock

2. Think of a different letter to complete the words in each set. Then write the words in alphabetical order.

a) com__uter   com__c   com__   com__and

b) cro__ked   cro__n   cro__k   cro__

c) sea__on   sea__ing   sea__ull   sea__orse

d) pla__ter   pla__er   pla__e   pla__ue

So – what have you learned about alphabetical order?

Focus

The ability to understand **rhyming** is important in spelling.

I **found** a p**ound** on the gr**ound**.

The bully was gr**uff** and t**ough**.

Often words that rhyme **look alike**.

Sometimes words **sound** similar but have **different letter patterns**.

Check it out

1. There are ten pairs of rhyming words in the word wall.
   Find them and write each pair in your book.

cross	mother	match	loud	wise	
	loft	proud	gush	bread	speak
care	head	brush	catch	soft	
	brother	moss	beak	rise	rare

Practice

1. Find the word in Set B that rhymes with a word in Set A.
   Write the pairs of rhyming words in your book.

Set A

chair   dear   knight
kind   laugh   loud   wrist
high   more   suit

Set B

pier   kissed   flute
cry   there   four   signed
crowd   bath   write

2. Now write one more rhyming word to go with each pair you
   have written.

Challenger

1. Copy the sets of words. Underline the odd
   word out in each set.

a) most   ghost   lost   post
b) cough   enough   tough   rough
c) mice   nice   twice   police
d) hive   give   five   arrive
e) bead   dead   head   thread
f) know   now   grow   blow
g) hear   dear   bear   fear
i) four   hour   sour   flour
j) root   shoot   foot   boot
k) rose   pose   nose   lose

So – what have you learned about rhyming?

Focus

A **suffix** is a group of letters we add to the **end** of a word.
Suffixes may **change the purpose** of the word.
Some **nouns** and **adjectives** may be changed into **verbs** by using different **suffixes**.

I put an advert in the paper to advert**ise** my bike.

My pencil is not sharp so I will sharp**en** it.

The suffix **ise** has been added to the noun 'advert' to make it into the verb 'advert**ise**'.

The suffix **en** has been added to the adjective 'sharp' to make it into the verb 'sharp**en**'.

Check it out

1. Make these adjectives into verbs by adding the suffix **en**.
   Do it like this: **dark + en = darken**

   a) fast   c) tight   e) quick   g) short
   b) soft   d) sharp   f) sweet   h) dead

2. Now try these – but be careful with the spellings!

   a) fat   b) loose   c) sad   d) wide

Objective ~ to recognise the way in which nouns and adjectives can be made into verbs by use of suffixes, e.g. 'ate'

Practice

1. Write the **ate** verb from which the following nouns come.

Do it like this: **complication – complicate**

a) desperation   d) communication   g) hesitation

b) operation   e) celebration   h) education

c) punctuation   f) indication   i) termination

2. Make up five sentences using some of the **ate** verbs you have found. Each sentence can contain more than one of the words.

Challenger

1. Write the root word from which each of these verbs is formed.

Do it like this: **advertise – advert**

a) categorise   e) equalise   i) glorify

b) simplify   f) legalise   j) amplify

c) magnetise   g) nationalise   k) characterise

d) purify   h) signify   l) dramatise

2. Choose the suffix **ate**, **ise** or **ify** to complete each word.

Use a dictionary, if necessary.

a) discrimin_____   d) superv_____   g) magn_____

b) horr_____   e) qual_____   h) econom_____

c) critic_____   f) isol_____   i) integr_____

3. Now write the meaning of each word you have just made.

Check your meanings in a dictionary.

So – what have you learned about the suffixes 'en', 'ate', 'ise', and 'ify'?

Focus

When a noun ends in **f** (or **fe**), we usually change the **f** to **v** and add **es** when we write it in the plural.

one loa**f**   lots of loa**ves**

NB: A few nouns ending in **f don't** follow this rule.

They just add **s** in the plural.

For example: **chiefs   roofs   handkerchiefs   waifs   gulfs**

Check it out

1. Copy and complete this table.

Singular	Plural
leaf	leaves
loaf	
calf	
	halves
thief	
	elves
shelf	
	scarves
wolf	

Practice

1. Write the singular form of each of these nouns in your book.

a) thieves   c) calves   e) knives   g) loaves
b) sheaves   d) wives   f) lives   h) shelves

2. Write the plural form of each of these nouns in your book.
   Think about them carefully.

a) self   c) wife   e) hoof   g) half
b) leaf   d) chief   f) wolf   h) waif

Challenger

1. Copy these sentences. Use the plural form of a noun ending in **f**
   to fill in each gap.

a) You need sharp _____ to cut tough meat.
b) The baker put out the freshly-baked _____ .
c) In autumn, many trees drop their _____ .
d) The cow gave birth to two _____ .
e) The _____ in the shop were laden with chocolates.
f) A cat is said to have nine _____ .
g) The pack of _____ roamed the forest.
h) A man who has two _____ is called a bigamist.
i) The cake was cut into two equal _____ .
j) Two _____ broke into the bank and stole some money.

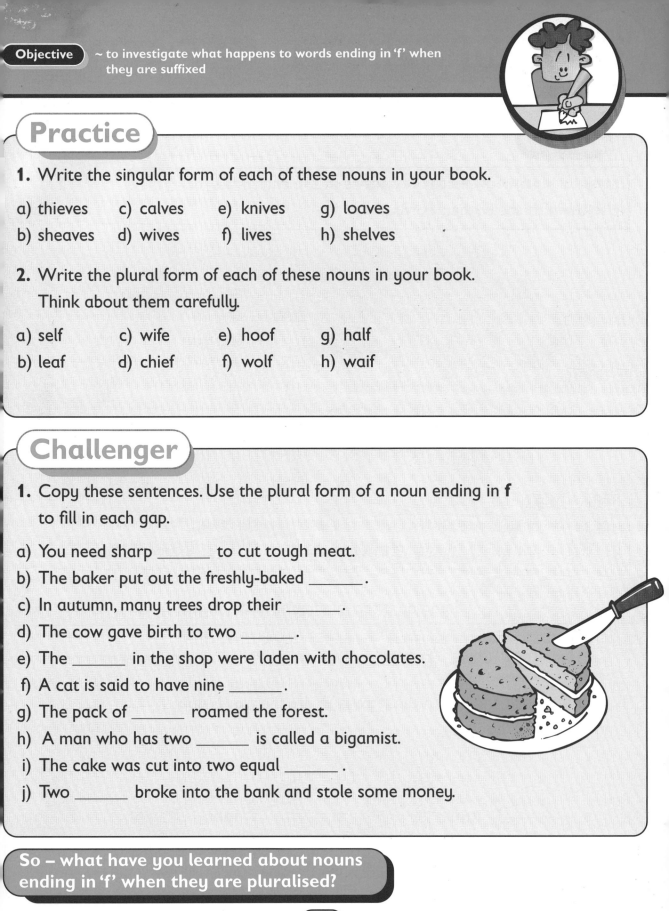

So – what have you learned about nouns
ending in 'f' when they are pluralised?

Focus

Look for **common letter patterns** at the ends of words.
Use them to spell other words.

Sam had a terrible fr**ight** in the n**ight**!

Check it out

1. Add the word endings to the letters. Write the words you make in your book.

f
r
s → **ight**
t
n

fl
fr
sl → **ight**
pl
del

Practice

1. Make some new words from these words you know.

a) Change the **m** in **more** to **w, b, sc, sh, st, sn, sw**.

b) Change the **c** in **care** to **d, sh, sc, squ, st, sp, fl, prep, bew**.

c) Change the **c** in **cage** to **w, r, st, eng, outr**.

d) Change the **f** in **face** to **l, p, r, pl, gr**.

2. Now write each set of new words you have made in alphabetical order.

Challenger

1. Find the eight **ure** words in the puzzle. Write them in your book.

2. Make up eight sentences. Use each of the **ure** words in your sentences at least once.

q	w	e	c	a	p	t	u	r	e	r	t
y	u	i	n	a	t	u	r	e	o	p	a
s	m	i	x	t	u	r	e	d	f	g	h
n	m	p	u	n	c	t	u	r	e	z	x
m	n	l	e	c	t	u	r	e	c	v	b
c	o	n	j	u	r	e	w	e	r	f	g
a	s	d	t	r	e	a	s	u	r	e	h
p	i	c	t	u	r	e	m	n	b	v	c

So – what have you learned about common word endings?

High frequency words

Focus

There are some **words** that we **often come across** in our **reading** and want to use in our **writing**. It is important to **recognise** these and know how to **spell** them.

I h**ear** with my **ear**!

These must be past tense. They all end in **ed**!

ask**ed**
jump**ed**
open**ed**

The apostrophe means something is missing.

can't = can not

In spelling, it helps to understand how **language is used** and to look out for **spelling patterns**.

Check it out

1. Match up the pairs of words with common letter patterns in Set A and Set B. Underline them. The first one has been done for you.

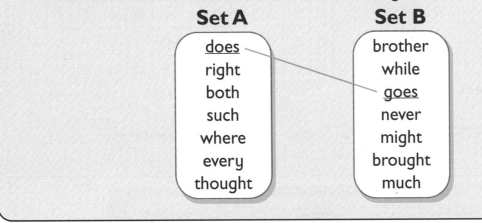

Set A	Set B
<u>does</u>	brother
right	while
both	<u>goes</u>
such	never
where	might
every	brought
thought	much

Practice

1. Write down the long form of these contractions in your book.

a) I'm   b) can't   c) didn't   d) don't

2. Write the past tense of the regular verbs below. Do it like this: **ask – asked**

a) live   c) open   e) stop   g) walk
b) jump   d) start   f) turn   h) use

3. Now write the past tense of these irregular verbs, but be careful!
   Do it like this: **find – found**.

a) say   c) begin   e) know   g) tell
b) bring   d) hear   f) think   h) wake

Challenger

1. Sort the words in the box into three groups, according to their prefixes.

> almost   below   across   between
> above   always   also   before   around

2. Copy these words. Underline the silent letter in each word.

a) know   b) write   c) half   d) watch

Think of one more word for each example that contains the same silent letter.

3. Divide the words in the box into groups of two- and three-syllable words.

> second   following   together   without
> outside   different   coming   suddenly

Think of five more words to add to each group.

So – what have you learned about spelling high frequency words?

Focus

Sometimes we can use the same word **too often** in a piece of writing.
Try to use other words that are more interesting or accurate.

When I **got** home, I **got** an apple and **got** on with my homework.

When I **arrived** home, I **picked up** an apple and **started** my homework.

In the first sentence the word **got** is used three times. The second sentence shows how it could be written without using the word at all.

Check it out

1. Rewrite the sentences below. Replace the word **good** in each sentence with a different word to make it more interesting.

a) It was a **good** television programme.

b) I had a **good** sleep.

c) The meal tasted very **good**.

d) The teacher said my work was **good**.

e) My dog is always **good** when we go out.

f) We had a **good** time at the museum.

g) The weather was **good** in the afternoon.

Practice

1. Rewrite each phrase in your book. Replace the word **nice** with another adjective each time. Do it like this: **a <u>nice</u> garden – a <u>beautiful</u> garden**

a) a nice garden

b) a nice cake

c) a nice walk

d) a nice house

e) a nice day

f) a nice book

2. Now make up six sentences. Use the new phrases in them at least once.

3. Rewrite these sentences. Replace the word **got** with something more interesting.

a) I got up at eight o'clock.

b) I got my breakfast early.

c) I got a bad cold last week.

d) I got to school late.

e) Mr and Mrs Patel got married in June.

f) "I haven't got your ball."

Challenger

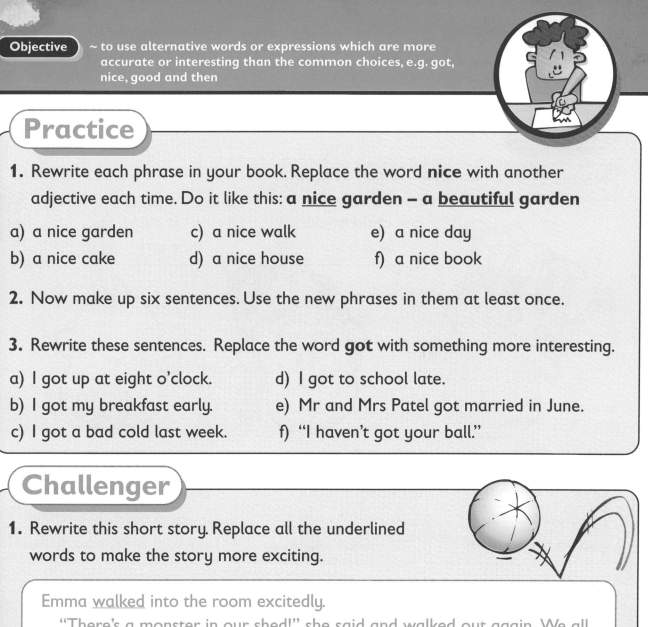

1. Rewrite this short story. Replace all the underlined words to make the story more exciting.

Emma <u>walked</u> into the room excitedly.

"There's a monster in our shed!" she <u>said</u> and <u>walked</u> out again. We all <u>went</u> after her. When we <u>got to</u> the shed, Emma was already there.

"Shall I open the door?" she <u>said</u>.

Suddenly, there was a loud banging noise. Emma <u>got hold of</u> the shed door and opened it. A strange-looking thing <u>came</u> out and <u>walked</u> towards us. "Whoooooooo!" it <u>said</u> in a loud voice as it <u>got</u> nearer. We <u>looked</u> at it in amazement.

Then the monster <u>went</u> into our house! When we <u>got there</u>, we <u>found</u> that the monster was really Sam dressed up!

So – what have you learned about avoiding over-used words?

Focus

Nouns may be divided according to gender.

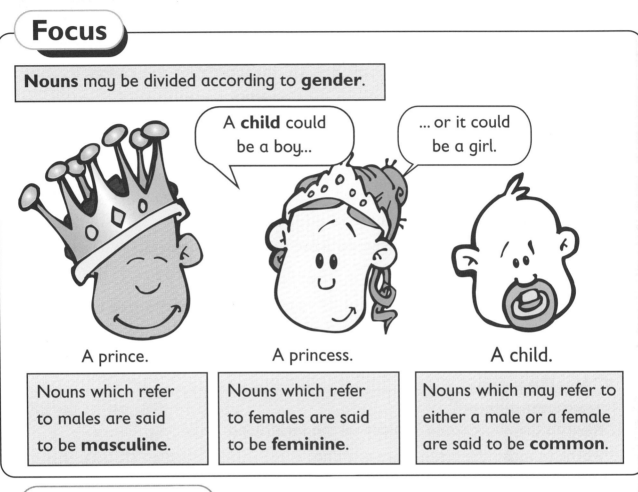

A **child** could be a boy...

... or it could be a girl.

A prince.

A princess.

A child.

| Nouns which refer to males are said to be **masculine**. | Nouns which refer to females are said to be **feminine**. | Nouns which may refer to either a male or a female are said to be **common**. |

Check it out

1. Copy this table.
Fill in the missing nouns.

Masculine	Feminine
man	woman
boy	
	mother
brother	
king	
	princess
	aunt
gentleman	
	wife

Practice

1. Match up and write the masculine and feminine names for each animal.

Masculine

boar   bull   cockerel
drake   fox   gander   lion
ram   stallion   tiger

Feminine

hen   goose   sow   vixen
mare   duck   tigress
lioness   cow   ewe

2. Copy the nouns below. After each noun say if it is masculine (M), feminine (F) like the first one or common (C).

a) niece (F)   d) nephew   g) nun   j) traveller

b) husband   e) teacher   h) friend   k) monk

c) child   f) bull   i) bride   l) lord

Challenger

1. Rewrite these sentences. Change the feminine nouns into masculine ones.

a) The princess went to the ball.

b) The bride arrived at the church.

c) The landlady at the hotel was very welcoming.

d) The cow was all alone in her field.

e) The headmistress went into her office.

2. Now rewrite these sentences. Change the masculine nouns into feminine ones.

a) Mr Smith sent his son a present.

b) The man bowed to the duke.

c) The fox was hunting for food for his family.

d) My uncle lives in Scotland with his wife.

So – what have you learned about gender?

Focus

New words enter our language all the time and old words fall out of use.

The girl wore a beautiful **bonnet**.

This word was common in the last century. We don't use it much today.

The girl wore a red **baseball** cap.

This is a new word to our language.

Check it out

1. Copy the word wall below. Underline the words which you think are new to our language.

	trainers	swimming	satellite
school	mountains	computer	
	video	the Internet	football
supermarket	school	virtual reality	

Practice

1. Here are the names of some occupations that are gradually dying out. Match up each job with the correct definition. Use a dictionary, if necessary.

A cobbler	is a blacksmith who shoes horses.
A cooper	sells tools, nails, screws, etc.
A farrier	makes or sells ladies' hats.
A hosier	mends pots and pans.
An ironmonger	makes and repairs shoes.
A milliner	makes barrels and casks.
A pedlar	sells stockings, socks and underwear.
A tinker	sells from door to door.

Challenger

1. These are all old words for different sorts of containers. Find out what each word means by looking in a dictionary. Write the words and their meanings in your book.

a) caddy   b) goblet   c) satchel   d) scabbard

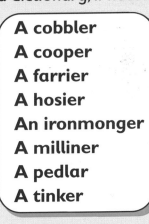

2. All of these old words are to do with fires. Write the words and what they mean in your book.

a) poker   b) tongs   c) fender   d) scuttle

3. These are all old names for rooms in a house. Write the words and what they mean in your book.

a) larder   b) scullery   c) parlour   d) garret

So – what have you learned about the way our language changes over time?

Focus

A **suffix** is a group of letters we add to the end of a word. Suffixes may **change the purpose** of the word. Some **nouns** and **verbs** may be changed into adjectives by using different **suffixes**.

It is danger**ous** to go any further.

DANGER

I'll have to **wash** your shorts! It's lucky they're wash**able**.

danger + ous = dangerous

We can make the **noun danger** into an **adjective** by adding the suffix **ous**.

wash + able = washable

We can make the **verb wash** into an **adjective** by adding the suffix **able**.

Check it out

1. Add the suffix **able** to these words to change them into adjectives.

Do it like this: **wash + able = washable**

a) crush   c) comfort   e) credit   g) remark

b) reason   d) suit   f) favour   h) fashion

2. Write the root word of each of these adjectives.

Do it like this: **dangerous – danger**

a) poisonous   b) mountainous   c) perilous   d) adventurous

Practice

1. Write the root word of each of these adjectives.

Do it like this: **famous – fame**

Be careful – there are some tricky ones!

a) noisy
b) reliable
c) victorious
d) miserable
e) envious
f) impulsive
g) childish
h) studious
i) energetic
j) volcanic
k) attractive
l) foolish

2. Now write the adjectives in question 1 above in six sets, according to their suffixes.

Challenger

1. Copy these sentences. Fill in each gap with an adjective ending in **ive**, **ous** or **ic**.

a) Sam was a good athlete. She was very _____.
b) Tom knew how to express himself. His writing was very _____.
c) Emma was filled with envy. She was very _____.
d) I have never seen anyone so full of energy. James was really _____.
e) The fox continued to elude the hunters. It was very _____.
f) Ben liked to study. He was very _____.
g) How _____! It was such a mystery!
h) The giant was huge. He was _____.

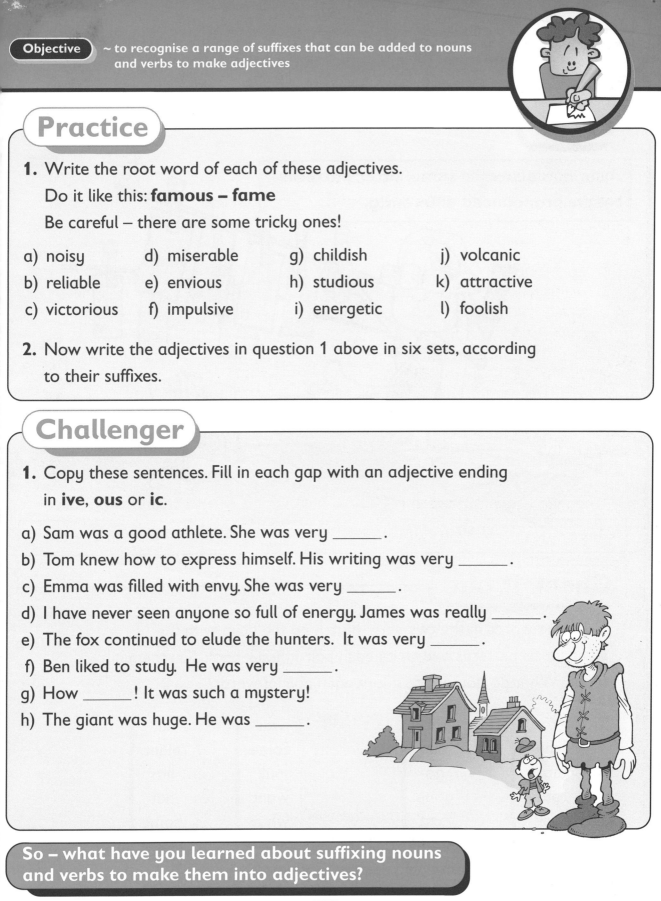

So – what have you learned about suffixing nouns and verbs to make them into adjectives?

Focus

Some words have the **same letter patterns** but are **pronounced differently**.

c**ash**   w**ash**

Check it out

1. Copy the words in the two sets. Match up the pairs with the same letter patterns and write each pair in your book. Say them aloud. What do you notice about each pair of words?

a)

to	the
she	cut
most	go
put	gone
one	cost

b)

was	dull
come	plant
pull	has
want	hat
what	home

2. Write a sentence containing each pair of words.

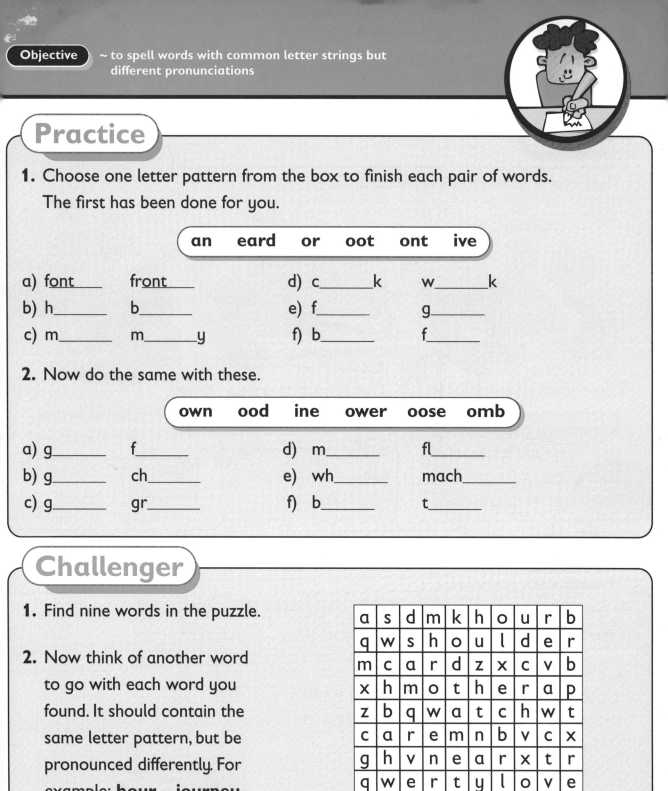

Practice

1. Choose one letter pattern from the box to finish each pair of words. The first has been done for you.

> **an   eard   or   oot   ont   ive**

a) f<u>ont</u>   fr<u>ont</u>   d) c_____k   w_____k

b) h_____   b_____   e) f_____   g_____

c) m_____   m_____y   f) b_____   f_____

2. Now do the same with these.

> **own   ood   ine   ower   oose   omb**

a) g_____   f_____   d) m_____   fl_____

b) g_____   ch_____   e) wh_____   mach_____

c) g_____   gr_____   f) b_____   t_____

Challenger

1. Find nine words in the puzzle.

2. Now think of another word to go with each word you found. It should contain the same letter pattern, but be pronounced differently. For example: **h<u>our</u> – jo<u>ur</u>ney**

a	s	d	m	k	h	o	u	r	b
q	w	s	h	o	u	l	d	e	r
m	c	a	r	d	z	x	c	v	b
x	h	m	o	t	h	e	r	a	p
z	b	q	w	a	t	c	h	w	t
c	a	r	e	m	n	b	v	c	x
g	h	v	n	e	a	r	x	t	r
q	w	e	r	t	y	l	o	v	e
p	o	h	e	a	d	u	y	t	r

So – what have you learned about looking carefully at letter patterns and listening to the way they are pronounced?

Focus

The letter **k** sometimes performs **different jobs** in words.

The sna**k**e ate a sna**ck**!

K is usually accompanied by a letter **c** if it has a **short vowel** sound **before** it (as in **snack**).

The **k**ing has a pet **k**angaroo and **c**at.

Sometimes it sounds like a **c** at the start of words.

The **k**night **k**new how to **k**nit.

Sometimes it isn't pronounced at all!

Check it out

1. Rewrite these sentences in your book. Choose the correct word in the brackets to complete each sentence.

a) You (back, bake) a pie in the oven.

b) My cat likes to (lick, like) milk from a saucer.

c) (Smock, Smoke) was coming out of the chimney.

d) The (duck, duke) quacked loudly.

e) Come for a swim in the (lack, lake).

f) He told me a funny (jock, joke).

g) (Luck, Luke) was a very nice boy.

h) (Jack, Jake) climbed the beanstalk.

i) I (picked, piked) the winning lottery ticket.

Practice

1. Add **k** to the beginning of these word endings. Write the words you make in your book.

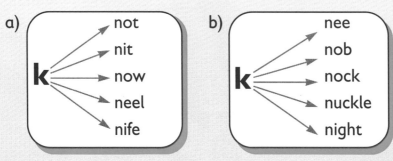

a)
k
→ not
→ nit
→ now
→ neel
→ nife

b)
k
→ nee
→ nob
→ nock
→ nuckle
→ night

2. Now write each set of words you have made in alphabetical order.

Challenger

1. Copy the words below. Choose **c** or **k** to begin each word and fill in the gap.

a) __ing   e) __ider   i) __itten   m) __elery

b) __ircle   f) __ement   j) __ell   n) __etchup

c) __ennel   g) __ettle   k) __inema   o) __eg

d) __itchen   h) __iss   l) __ite   p) __ircus

2. Say each word aloud. Write a sentence to explain what you notice when the second letter of the word is **e** or **i**.

3. Choose three words beginning with **c** and three words beginning with **k**. Write six sentences using the words you have chosen.

So – what have you learned about the letter 'k'?

Focus

The letters **a** and **o** are often pronounced differently after the letter **w**.

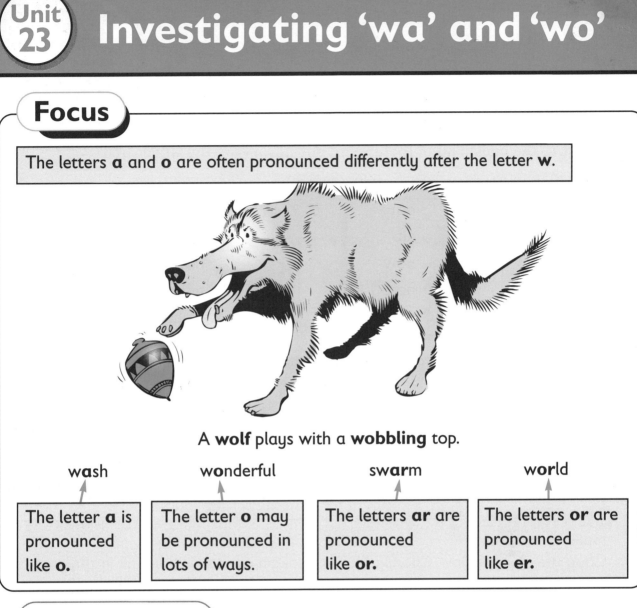

A **wolf** plays with a **wobbling** top.

| w**a**sh | w**o**nderful | sw**ar**m | w**or**ld |

The letter **a** is pronounced like **o**.

The letter **o** may be pronounced in lots of ways.

The letters **ar** are pronounced like **or**.

The letters **or** are pronounced like **er**.

Check it out

1. Copy the words in the word wall.

Complete each word with the letter **a**.

w__nt	w__s	w__sh	w__nder
	w__sp	w__llet	w__ddle	
w__d	sw__n	sw__mp	sw__llow

2. Choose five of the words and write out a different sentence for each one.

Practice

1. Copy the words below. Write a definition for each word.
Use a dictionary, if necessary.

a) wobble   c) won   e) worry   g) womb

b) wombat   d) wonderful   f) wolf   h) woman

2. How many different ways is the letter **o** pronounced in the
words above? Write the words in sets according to their sounds.

Challenger

1. Copy these words. Choose **ar** or **or** to complete each word.

a) w____k   e) w____th   i) dw____f

b) rew____d   f) w____rant   j) w____m

c) sw____m   g) w____p   k) w____d

d) w____thy   h) w____e   l) w____n

2. Which four words can take both **ar** and **or**?

3. Write what you notice about the way **ar** and **or** are
pronounced in the words you have made.

4. Write as many words as you can which begin with **w** and are
followed by the following phonemes.

a) ai   b) oo   c) ou

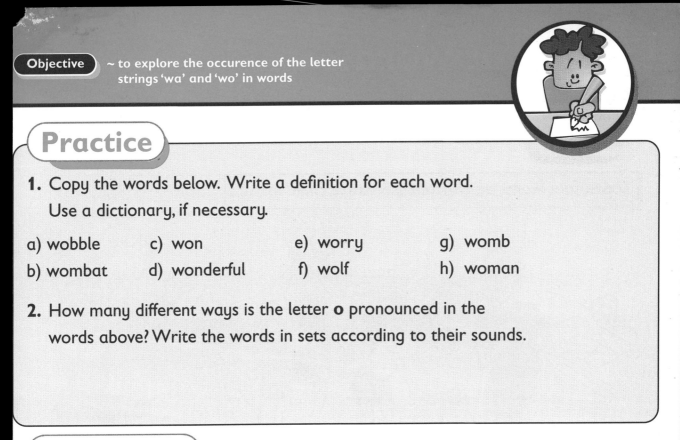

WANTED

DEAD OR ALIVE
$10,000

So – what have you learned about the letter patterns 'wa' and 'wo'?

49

Focus

Sometimes words come from the **same root word**.

helpful   **help**less   **help**er   un**help**ful

These words all share the same root word: **help**.

Check it out

1. Copy these sets of words in your book. Underline the common root word in each, like the first one.

a) <u>know</u>ing	un<u>know</u>n	<u>know</u>ledge
b) advent	invent	prevent
c) pressing	depress	pressure
d) marked	marks	remarkable
e) disagree	agreeable	agreement
f) clearly	clearance	unclear
g) cheaply	cheapen	cheaper
h) photograph	telegraph	autograph

Practice

1. Many ...ve Latin roots. Copy the table and fill in the words from the ... the correct columns. The first one has been done for you.

Latin word	Meaning	English words which come from it
signum	mark	sign signal
specto	I look	
tractum	drawn away	
scribo	I write	
verbum	word	

verbal
spectator
inscribe
proverb
sign
subtract
signal
manuscript
detract
spectacles

2. Think of one more word you could put in each column of the table you have just completed above.

Challenger

1. Here are some more Latin roots, and one word which comes from each. Think of as many more English words as possible which come from the same root. Write your words in your book.

Latin word	Meaning	English words which come from it
positum	placed	deposit
pendeo	I hang	suspend
terra	land	terrace
primus	first	prime
annus	year	annual
civis	citizen	civic
fortis	strong	fortify

So – what have you learned about root words?

Focus

We can make some words longer by adding a **prefix** at the beginning or a **suffix** at the end.

happy

unhappy

happi**ness**

| This is the root word. | We can add a prefix. | We can add a suffix. |

Check it out

1. Copy the words below. Choose **un** or **dis** to fill in each gap.

a) __agree   c) __dress   e) __obey

b) __trust   d) __do   f) __fair

2. Copy the words below. Choose **re** or **de** to fill in each gap.
(One can take both.)

a) __place   c) __form   e) __face

b) __parted   d) __trace   f) __call

Practice

1. Copy these words. Then write each word without its suffix.

Do it like this: **crunchy – crunch**

a) funnily   d) older   g) merciful   j) angrily

b) noisy   e) bravest   h) pitiless   k) artist

c) starry   f) heavier   i) simply   l) drummer

2. Give these words the opposite meaning by changing the suffix.
Write the new words in your book.

a) hopeful   c) useful   e) harmless   g) thankless

b) powerful   d) cheerful   f) colourless   h) merciless

Challenger

1. Extend each word below by adding a prefix. Write the words in
your book. Do it like this: **dress – undress**

a) behave   c) obey   e) calculate   g) caution

b) port   d) order   f) hale   h) posit

2. Extend each word below by adding a suffix. Do it like this: **slow – slowly**

a) fault   c) nice   e) hungry   g) act

b) empty   d) miserable   f) call   h) swim

3. Extend each word by adding a prefix and a suffix to it.
Do it like this: **help – unhelpful**

a) happy   c) judge   e) cover   g) count

b) vent   d) stand   f) turn   h) health

So – what have you learned about extending
words by adding prefixes and suffixes?

Focus

Two common suffixes are **able** and **ible**.

comfort + able = comfortable

It is often possible to see the whole root word when the suffix **able** is added.

terror + ible = terrible

It is often not possible to see the whole root word when the suffix **ible** is added.

Check it out

1. Copy these word sums in your book. Write the answers.

a) reason + able = _____

b) fashion + able = _____

c) remark + able = _____

d) favour + able = _____

e) obtain + able = _____

f) consider + able = _____

g) punish + able = _____

h) laugh + able = _____

2. Copy these words in your book. Write the root word from which each came. Do it like this: **believable – believe**

a) copiable

b) excitable

c) valuable

d) reliable

e) manageable

f) miserable

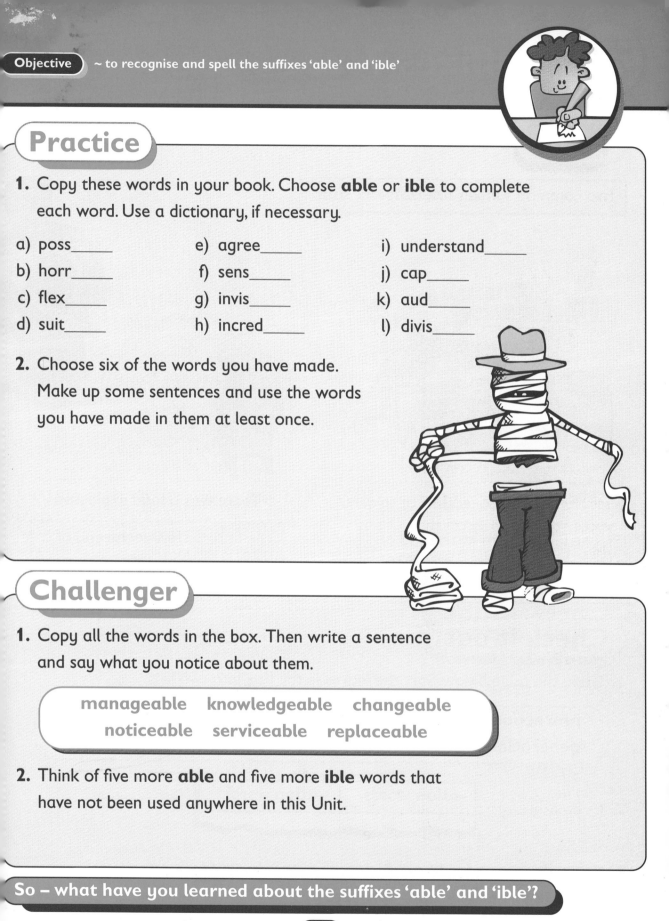

Practice

1. Copy these words in your book. Choose **able** or **ible** to complete each word. Use a dictionary, if necessary.

a) poss_____

b) horr_____

c) flex_____

d) suit_____

e) agree_____

f) sens_____

g) invis_____

h) incred_____

i) understand_____

j) cap_____

k) aud_____

l) divis_____

2. Choose six of the words you have made.
Make up some sentences and use the words
you have made in them at least once.

Challenger

1. Copy all the words in the box. Then write a sentence
and say what you notice about them.

> manageable   knowledgeable   changeable
> noticeable   serviceable   replaceable

2. Think of five more **able** and five more **ible** words that
have not been used anywhere in this Unit.

So – what have you learned about the suffixes 'able' and 'ible'?

Focus

Two common suffixes are **tion** and **sion**.

Sam has a large collec**tion** of spiders.

The letters **tion** at the end of a word sounds like **shun**.

There was a loud explo**sion**.

The letters **sion** at the end of a word sounds like **zhun**.

Check it out

1. Copy the table below. Sort the words in the box into two sets.

> protection   creation   education   collection   direction
>
> generation   action   inspection   decoration   organisation

–ction words	–ation words

2. Write the root word from which each of the words comes.

   Do it like this: **protection – protect**

Practice

1. Copy this table in your book. Change each of the verbs into a noun ending in **sion**.

Verb	Noun ending in **sion**
televise	television
decide	
include	
confuse	
provide	
explode	
divide	
erode	
deride	
invade	

Challenger

1. Copy the words below. Choose **tion** or **sion** to complete each word. Use a dictionary, if necessary.

a) imagina____   e) competi____   i) conversa____

b) exhibi____   f) separa____   j) ventila____

c) occa____   g) seclu____   k) inci____

d) revi____   h) cohe____   l) illu____

2. Think of six words that end in **ssion** and write them in your books.

So – what have you learned about the suffixes 'tion' and 'sion'?

Focus

People often confuse **its** and **it's**. It is important to learn the difference!

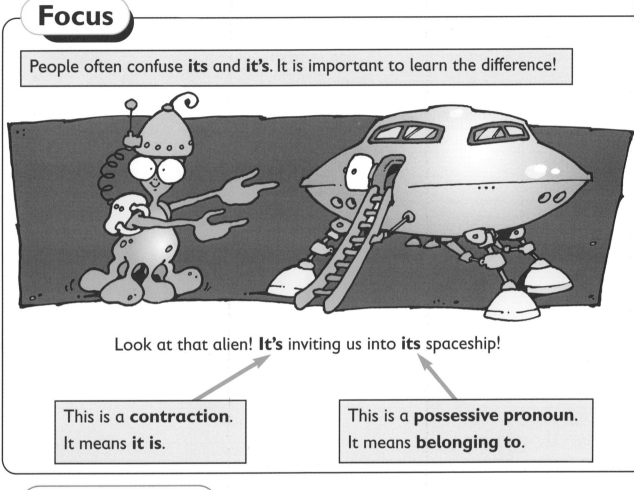

Look at that alien! **It's** inviting us into **its** spaceship!

This is a **contraction**.
It means **it is**.

This is a **possessive pronoun**.
It means **belonging to**.

Check it out

1. Copy these sentences. Choose **it's** or **its** to fill in each gap.

a) "____ a lovely day today," Mrs Saunders said.

b) The dog wagged ____ tail.

c) The car had got a scratch on ____ door.

d) I think ____ good to be able to play a musical instrument.

e) If ____ raining, I stay indoors.

f) The puppy could not find ____ owner.

g) "Come on! ____ time for lunch!" Emma shouted.

h) ____ not nice to tell lies.

Practice

1. Copy this short story. Fill in each gap correctly with **its** or **it's**.

The mouse was small but _____ tail was long and so were _____ whiskers. It had a white patch on _____ tummy. _____ ears were pink. It poked _____ nose out of _____ hole and said, "I think _____ time I went for a walk. _____ nearly teatime so I'll see what I can find to eat."

Off it went on _____ way, stopping now and again to check it was safe. It had no idea that _____ enemy, the cat, was just round the corner.

The cat was just washing _____ face. "_____ time for some fun," it said as it saw the mouse. "_____ dinnertime!"

The cat screeched and jumped at the mouse.

"I think _____ time to go," the mouse shouted as it turned and raced for home.

"_____ no use running away! I'm too fast for you," the cat said.

But luckily for the mouse, it reached _____ hole first and raced inside just as the cat was going to grab _____ tail.

Challenger

1. Make up five sentences of your own containing **it's**.

2. Make up five sentences of your own containing **its**.
    Compare and check your sentences with a partner.

So – what have you learned about 'its' and 'it's'?

Focus

A **compound word** is a word which is made up of **two smaller words** joined together.

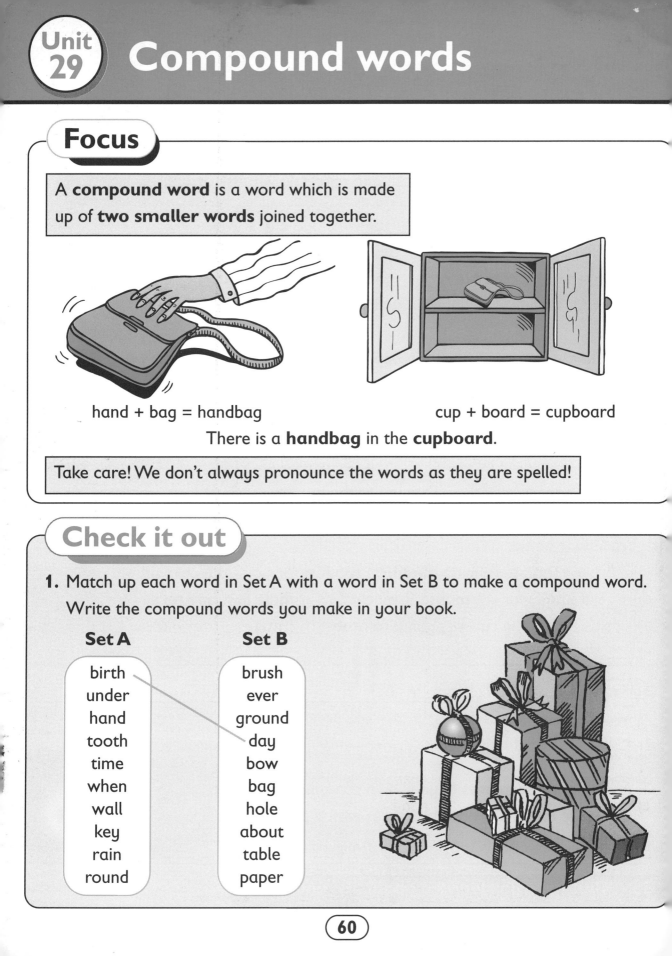

hand + bag = handbag

cup + board = cupboard

There is a **handbag** in the **cupboard**.

Take care! We don't always pronounce the words as they are spelled!

Check it out

1. Match up each word in Set A with a word in Set B to make a compound word. Write the compound words you make in your book.

Set A	Set B
birth	brush
under	ever
hand	ground
tooth	day
time	bow
when	bag
wall	hole
key	about
rain	table
round	paper

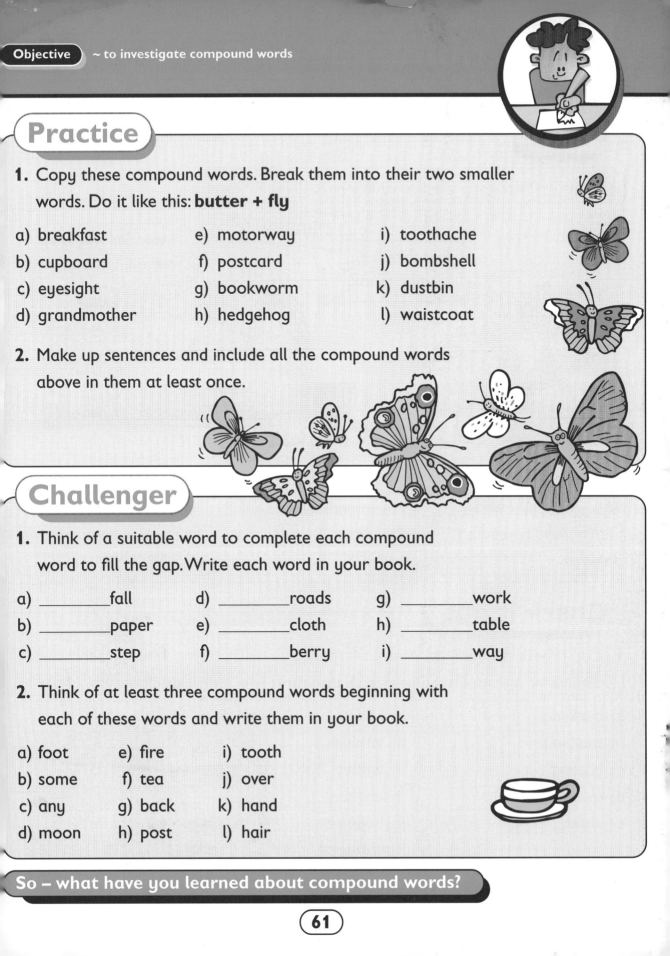

Practice

1. Copy these compound words. Break them into their two smaller words. Do it like this: **butter + fly**

a) breakfast   e) motorway   i) toothache

b) cupboard   f) postcard   j) bombshell

c) eyesight   g) bookworm   k) dustbin

d) grandmother   h) hedgehog   l) waistcoat

2. Make up sentences and include all the compound words above in them at least once.

Challenger

1. Think of a suitable word to complete each compound word to fill the gap. Write each word in your book.

a) _____fall   d) _____roads   g) _____work

b) _____paper   e) _____cloth   h) _____table

c) _____step   f) _____berry   i) _____way

2. Think of at least three compound words beginning with each of these words and write them in your book.

a) foot   e) fire   i) tooth

b) some   f) tea   j) over

c) any   g) back   k) hand

d) moon   h) post   l) hair

So – what have you learned about compound words?

Focus

Diminutives are words that imply something small.

Minimarket

Is a minimum a small mum?

I wonder why they call me Little John!

a duck and a duckling

We sometimes make diminutives by adding a **suffix**.

minimarket

We sometimes make diminutives by adding a **prefix**.

Little John

We sometimes make diminutives by adding an **adjective**.

Check it out

1. Copy these diminutives. Write a sentence for each, saying what you think each diminutive means. Do it like this: **A duckling is a small duck**

a) duckling

b) seedling

c) gosling

d) owlet

e) piglet

f) streamlet

g) hillock

h) lambkin

i) leaflet

j) eaglet

k) booklet

l) statuette

2. Check your meanings in a dictionary.

Practice

1. Match up and write the pairs of diminutives in your book, according to their common suffixes.

bullock	codling	lambkin	hillock	
	ringlet	kitten	kitchenette	napkin
morsel	laddie	maiden	nestling	
	lassie	leaflet	damsel	statuette

2. Choose five diminutives from the wall and explain what each one means. Use a dictionary, if necessary.

Challenger

1. Write five words which begin with the prefix **mini**.

2. Make up the names, or nicknames, for some characters which imply smallness, e.g. Little John, Tiny Tim, Titch, Mini Midge, Shorty, etc.

3. Match up each adult animal with its young. Use a dictionary, if necessary.

Adult				Young		
bear	cat	deer		elver	kitten	lamb
elephant	duck	eel		fawn	kid	filly
frog	goat	hare		tadpole	calf	cygnet
mare	sheep	swan		leveret	cub	duckling

So – what have you learned about diminutives?

Range of Books Available

Year 3 Sentence	Year 4 Sentence	Year 5 Sentence	Year 6 Sentence
Year 3 Word	Year 4 Word	Year 5 Word	Year 6 Word

Literacy Differentiation Word Level Year 4

First published 1999
Reprinted 1999

Letts Educational,
9–15 Aldine Street, London W12 8AW
Tel: 020 8740 2270   Fax: 202 8740 2280

Illustrations © Richard Duszczak, David Lock, Tim Oliver, John Plumb, Sylvie Poggio Artists Agency (Simon Jacobs) and Ken Vail Graphic Design (Liz Bryan)

Designed by Ken Vail Graphic Design, Cambridge

British Library Cataloguing-in-Publication Data
A CIP record for this book is available from the British Library

ISBN: 1 84085 233 X

Printed in the UK by Bath Press Limited

Letts Educational is the trading name of BPP [Letts Educational] Ltd

**fold out flap
for your
spell checker**

Teaching and Learning
Key Stage 2
Differentiated Activity Book

Letts
EDUCATIONAL

Literacy

This Literacy Differentiated Activity Book for Word Level activities has been specifically written to help meet the requirements of the National Literacy Framework Strategy and supports the teaching of the Literacy Hour.

The book contains 30 units of work, sufficient for one school year, providing work for whole class, group or individual work. Each unit is straightforward and easy to use, offering:

- A teaching objective
- A clear teaching focus, with examples
- Differentiated activities for each objective at foundation, intermediate and challenging levels of difficulty
- A reminder of the main objective of the unit
- A fold out, ready reference flap inside the back cover

Letts Differentiated Activity Books are also available for:

Year 3 Word	Year 4 Word	Year 5 Word	Year 6 Word
Year 3 Sentence	Year 4 Sentence	Year 5 Sentence	Year 6 Sentence

£4.00

Louis Fidge and Ray Barker

ISBN 1 84085 233-X
9 781840 852332